BOTANICAL
DAY BOOK

ILLUSTRATED BY
GILLIAN BARLOW

LEOPARD

Personal Details

Name _____

Address _____

_____

Telephone (Home) _____ (Business) _____

National Insurance No. _____

Passport No. _____

Driving Licence No. _____

Bank Sort Code & Account No. _____

Address _____

Telephone _____

Doctor _____

Address _____

Telephone _____

Dentist _____

_____

Telephone _____

First published in Great Britain in 1995 by Leopard Books
Random House, 20 Vauxhall Bridge Road, London SW1V 2SA

Copyright © Random House UK Ltd 1995
Illustrations © Gilliam Barlow 1995

Typeset in Copperplate Gothic by
SX Composing Ltd, Rayleigh, Essex
Printed and bound in Singapore

ISBN 07529 0089 7

Cover illustration: *Rosa macrophylla.*

Introduction

THE ART OF BOTANICAL ILLUSTRATION, WHICH BEGAN IN EUROPE IN THE 15TH CENTURY, REACHED A PEAK OF ACHIEVEMENT IN THE 19TH WHEN SOME OF THE FINEST EXAMPLES WERE CREATED BY ARTISTS LIKE PIERRE JOSEPH REDOUTE. IT IS A BRANCH OF PAINTING CAPABLE OF PRODUCING RAVISHING WORKS OF ART, AND WHICH COMBINES SOME VERY SPECIAL SKILLS. THE FINEST EXAMPLES CAPTURE THE INHERENT BEAUTY OF THE FLOWERS THEMSELVES, AND SHOW AN UNDERSTANDING OF THE PLANT'S BOTANICAL CHARACTERISTICS. THEY ALSO SHOW A SENSE OF COMPOSITION AND DESIGN, AND GO BEYOND THE MERELY REPRESENTATIONAL TO PRODUCE PAINTINGS WHICH CAN MOVE AND DELIGHT US PROFOUNDLY.

THE GREAT AGE OF FLOWER PAINTING IN THE 18TH AND 19TH CENTURIES COINCIDED, FOR OBVIOUS REASONS, WITH A HUGE GROWTH OF INTEREST IN BOTANY IN GENERAL. AS TRAVEL THROUGHOUT THE WORLD BECAME LESS TROUBLESOME AND EXPENSIVE, PLANT-HUNTING EXPEDITIONS BROUGHT BACK SPECIMENS FROM EVERY CORNER OF THE GLOBE, BOTANICAL GARDENS WERE CREATED TO STUDY AND GROW THEM, AND BOTANICAL SCIENCE TOOK HUGE STRIDES FORWARDS. MANY OF THE PLANT-HUNTERS WERE IN A SENSE AMATEURS; AND MANY FINE FLOWER PAINTERS WERE EQUALLY UNINTERESTED IN EXPLOITING OR SELLING THEIR WORK.

TODAY, DESPITE CONSTANT REFINEMENT OF THE TECHNIQUE OF PLANT PHOTOGRAPHY, PAINTING IS OFTEN PREFERRED FOR SCIENTIFIC ILLUSTRATION. AN ARTIST CAN DISCRIMINATE BETWEEN IMPORTANT AND IRRELEVANT DETAIL MORE USEFULLY THAN THE CAMERA, AND CAN ALSO PRESENT THE INFORMATION IN A VISUALLY PLEASING WAY.

THERE ARE MANY FINE CONTEMPORARY BOTANICAL ARTISTS. THIS BOOK SHOWS THE RECENT WORK OF GILLIAN BARLOW WHO STUDIED PAINTING AT THE SLADE SCHOOL. SOME YEARS LATER SHE BEGAN PAINTING FLOWERS, BUILDING ON AN INTEREST AWAKENED BY HER BOTANIST FATHER, AND SOON DEVELOPED THIS MORE SERIOUSLY IN HER WORK. IN 1994 SHE WAS AWARDED THE ROYAL HORTICULTURAL SOCIETY'S GOLD MEDAL FOR BOTANICAL PAINTING, AND IS CURRENTLY WORKING FOR A SOLO EXHIBITION IN LONDON.

JANUARY

1

2

3

4

5

ROSA GLAUCA

JANUARY

6

7

8

9

10

January

11

12

13

14

15

JANUARY

16

17

18

19

20

PASSION FLOWER

JANUARY

21

22

23

24

25

JANUARY

26

27

28

29

30

31

1

2

3

4

February

IRIS ENSATA

5

6

7

8

9

FEBRUARY

10

11

12

13

14

FEBRUARY

15

16

17

18

19

ROSA 'MARGUERITE HILLINGS'

FEBRUARY

20

21

22

23

24

25

26

27

28

29

MARCH

1

2

3

4

5

TULIPA TARDA

6

7

8

9

10

March

11

12

13

14

15

MARCH

16

17

18

19

20

MARCH

ROSA MUNDI

MARCH

21

22

23

24

25

MARCH

26

27

28

29

30

31

1

2

3

4

IRIS SIBIRICA

APRIL

5

6

7

8

9

APRIL

10

11

12

13

14

APRIL

15

16

17

18

19

ROSA MICRANTHA

APRIL

20

21

22

23

24

APRIL

25

26

27

28

29

APR—MAY

30

1

2

3

4

PARROT TULIP

5

6

7

8

9

MAY

10

11

12

13

14

15

16

17

18

19

MAY

CALTHA PALUSTRIS

MAY

20

21

22

23

24

MAY

25

26

27

28

29

30

31

1

2

3

ROSA 'QUEEN ELIZABETH'

JUNE

4

5

6

7

8

JUNE

9

10

11

12

13

JUNE

14

15

16

17

18

JUNE

Helleborus foetidus

JUNE

19

20

21

22

23

JUNE

24

25

26

27

28

29

30

1

2

3

JULY

ROSA SPINOSISSIMA

JULY

4

5

6

7

8

JULY

9

10

11

12

13

JULY

14

15

16

17

18

Helleborus niger

JULY

19

20

21

22

23

JULY

24

25

26

27

28

JULY—AUG

29

30

31

1

2

DELPHINIUM CHINENSIS

AUGUST

3

4

5

6

7

AUGUST

8

9

10

11

12

AUGUST

13

14

15

16

17

ROSA MACROPHYLLA

AUGUST

18

19

20

21

22

AUGUST

23

24

25

26

27

28

29

30

31

1

September

Clematis viticella

September

2

3

4

5

6

SEPTEMBER

7

8

9

10

11

12

13

14

15

16

FRITILLARIA MELEAGRIS

SEPTEMBER

17

18

19

20

21

September

22

23

24

25

26

27

28

29

30

1

SUTHERLANDIA

October

2

3

4

5

6

OCTOBER

7

8

9

10

11

12

13

14

15

16

CORYDALIS FLEXUOSA

OCTOBER

17

18

19

20

21

OCTOBER

22

23

24

25

26

OCTOBER

27

28

29

30

31

OCTOBER

G.BARLOW · 1990

HIPPEASTRUM

November

1

2

3

4

5

November

6

7

8

9

10

NOVEMBER

11

12

13

14

15

NICOTIANA

NOVEMBER

16

17

18

19

20

NOVEMBER

21

22

23

24

25

26

27

28

29

30

BEARDED IRIS

DECEMBER

1

2

3

4

5

December

6

7

8

9

10

December

11

12

13

14

15

CHAENOMELES SPECIOSA 'NIVALIS'

December

16

17

18

19

20

December

21

22

23

24

25

26

27

28

29

30

31